POEMS AND STORIES

Poems and Stories

THOMAS McAFEE

NEW WRITERS SERIES

UNIVERSITY OF MISSOURI PRESS • COLUMBIA

ACKNOWLEDGMENTS: Thanks are due the following periodicals in whose pages some of these poems and stories originally appeared: *Approach, Beloit Poetry Journal, Compass Review, Contact, The Dial, Esquire* ("The Prisoner" was first published in *Esquire,* April 1959), *Gambit, The Montevallo Review, New Mexico Quarterly, Perspective, Prairie Schooner, Story, University of Kansas City Review, Western Review.*

Library of Congress Catalog Card Number 60-11579

Manufactured in the United States of America

for

ROBERT GRADY MCAFEE
and in memory of
ETHEL HALEY MCAFEE

PUBLISHER'S FOREWORD

THIS COLLECTION of poems and stories by Thomas McAfee is the first in a projected series of work by new young writers to be published by the University of Missouri Press. In America today the young writer is confronted with a peculiar and potentially destructive dilemma: more and more young American writers are creating meaningful poetry and fiction at a time when rapidly spiralling production costs make it increasingly difficult for them to reach a national audience. With its "New Writers Series," the University of Missouri Press hopes, in a modest way, to present to a national audience representative selections from the work of such young writers.

James Thomas McAfee was born in Haleyville, Alabama, in 1928. After graduation from Columbia Military Academy, Columbia, Tennessee, in 1945, he studied at the University of Missouri, where he received the A.B. in 1949 and the M.A. in 1950. Following his return from military service he taught in the English department at the University of Missouri where he is presently an assistant professor. Although *Poems and Stories* is his first published book, his works have appeared in many national magazines including *Contact, Dial, Esquire,* the *New Mexico Quarterly,* and *Story.*

This first book in the "New Writers Series" was made possible through the generosity of the late J. Breckenridge Ellis, Missouri novelist and graduate of the University of Missouri.

Contents

POEMS

I.

The Matriarch, 3

The Saga, 4

Semblances, 5

A Dream of the South, 6

The Photograph of My Grandparents, 8

The Porch of My Grandparents, 9

My Grandmother on the Porch of the
    Old Folks' Home, 10

A Foot of Earth, 11

II.

Early Retirement on North Street, 15

Fragment About Poetry, 16

The Last Peacock's Last Feather, 17

The Song of Painter X, 18

The Unhappy Few, 19

Song of Warlock, the Poet, 20

Bats in the Philippines, 21

Alas Poor Hogan, 22

III.

Oenone: To Her Statue, 25

Words for Penelope, 26

Zeus, 27

IV.

Poem to Myself, from an Ordinary Scene, 31

To My Godson, 32

Poem for My Father, 33

Greatness Tends to Slink, 34

Original Sin, 35

From the Pier . . . , 36

Much of My Anguish . . . , 37

To A Child, 38

The Alchemy, 39

Youth and the Tragic View, 40

Like Tributaries . . . , 41

From "Variations," 42

Dirge, 43

Sunday, 45

A Narrow World . . . , 47

v.

Borders and Peripheries

    The Border, 51

    There are Peripheries . . . , 52

    Above and Beyond Miss Rowland's, 53

    At Table . . . , 55

    Housecleaning, 56

    Back Home, and Reading, 58

    In Time of Sickness, 59

    The Day Before My Mother's Funeral, 61

    There Was A Lady, 62

STORIES

    The Hitch-Hiker, 65

    Suffer the Little Children, 72

    The Prisoner, 77

    Honest Dirt, 89

    Views, 99

    This is My Living Room, 105

I

You in your bounty—your hair scented gray—
Walked tall among petunias and your boys.
Slender, Bible-quoting, you had your say
On wars and marriage vows and proper toys
For grandchildren.

      When you family-prayed on Sunday nights—
The living room a crowd of things to do—
Each prudely solemn word defined your rights.
Tense wives cursed the scent of lavender, and the blue
You wore. But you ignored any narrowed eye
Which sparkled out against the truths you made.

Good woman: boys get bored, petunias seed, we die.
You did, holding tight to things that fade.
At your grave, veiled wives stood rigid, wanting to know
Why their glad husbands wept to see you go.

Aunt Alice big as a barrel,
Always an old-dress smell—
Sweat and rose cologne—

Was gallic when she met me,
With smothering hugs and kisses,
Too wet and adoring.

I'd run away from her.
"Where is the child, where?"
As I shook behind the juniper.

But sometimes she was fun:
A casket lid undone,
She cried and screamed like sixty.

For funerals were her game:
Petals nearly drooping
Before her happy rage.

Now my sons hide from her
(Her generation's dead),
Hide behind my legs.

And I must lift them up—
Almost in sacrifice—
To smother in her bosom.

Authority of roses protects us from
Our rural selves: we take off overalls
And denim shirts to admire the rose bushes.

On Sunday afternoons we put on a dark blue tie,
Gray trousers, to greet guests beside the blossoms.
Ladies delight at the "Talisman"
And we delight ourselves at playing gentlemen.
A drink in hand, proper words in our mouths
We convince ourselves of our meaning.

All this is important, even though
Night may find us brutal,
Throwing shoes at a bathroom wall,
Cursing through the door
At a wife in bed and crying.

Although divine disunity
Reigns there—the broganed
One-eyed man explains
Courtly gestures to a child,
A sunken garden shelters
Rusty fenders—although
Time itself has ruptured,
The feelers of my brain
Reach back to the sun.

It is unpleasant spring
Here in this other country.
Just a few of the trees
Have budded, only
Crocuses have bloomed.
There's been cold rain
Each day for a week.
    But a month ago, a letter
Told me:
            The jonquils
Are all in bloom.
Tom, you should see
The tulips. They're . . .

I see cold rain
Through a window
That goes darker;
I know that this ordered

World is corrupt,
It will not grow,
The sun won't corrupt it.

I think of pine trees,
I think of margins of flowers,
I long for a horse grazing,
I reach back to the sun.

THE PHOTOGRAPH OF MY GRANDPARENTS

To hide the sooted fireplace stood their youth,
A photograph within an ornate frame.
Whatever meaning pictures have, what truth
To last beyond a life, was here to blame.

Posed beside her, taller, and serene,
He was defiance for the hardest year;
And she, dressed in a gown that once was clean,
Looked fiercely straight into the far and near.

When I saw the picture last, her gown
Was speckled with the ash of many fires;
And dust and web-cracks made a smiling clown
Of that serenity which time admires.

Search out the farthest rooms and you will find
Not anywhere the action and the guilt.
The photograph is stored away, and kind
To them. This is the falling house they built.

They built destruction in disguise: bleached gray,
Long-splintered, marked with ragged rain-drop
      stains,
This porch that sags, and dips us when we walk,
Towards all the underneath grotesqueries:
Sick powder earth long years untouched by sun,
Black beetles, fortresses of spider webs.
And what we could not sweep away,
That slipped unnoticed underneath the broom,
Between the cracks: the dirty string, dead flies,
The vulgar yellowed paper. Cheap magazines
Are here beneath this honest porch. Pathos
And obscenity remain of what we thought
Was truly tragic, truly Grecian.
But now the sloping boards recall for us
What really was and what remains, what is,
We cannot rip away with axe and hammer
But wait for cigarette or wind or rain.

MY GRANDMOTHER ON THE PORCH
OF THE OLD FOLKS' HOME

The center of the group, you sit
Too proudly, almost like a queen.
The others in attendance seem
To wait. What will you say? I know
The haughty straightness is not real
And you are posed for all the world
To see your heart is still in one.
Come down! I know the flashing-red
Anger in your soul. I know
That age humiliates. I know
They took some poison from your hand
And kept you as their haughty queen.

I.

A foot of earth emancipates the mind:
Steeple, cupid, orthodoxies calm,

And bitter light falls gently on the eye.
First revelation, cunningly withheld?

As true apocrypha as intellect,
The only sure, and boundlessly immense.

II.

A foot of earth sets fire a gristled eye,
Trims out obscurity, defines the dust.

And set among beginnings of the rose,
The crumbling ear admits a final sound:

Each toll puts time more soundlessly away,
And hastens off the final winding-sheet.

II

The house I lived in hadn't a lawn or porch;
It rose straight up from sidewalk into sky.
At night cars idled, voices floated in,
But floated out more quickly, to my ease.
Sometimes a nightmare woke me up to hear
Quiet or the quietening street—sometimes
The clock tick measuring out the dark.
                                    And though
My room was almost bare, the rent was cheap.
I cherished those four peeling walls which kept
Me close to life yet far enough away.

FRAGMENT ABOUT POETRY

Out of his own irrelevance he wove
Down the chaotic snow-fallen street.
It was irregular there for snow at all,
And his feet were not made for the slickness.
He fell several times, belching.
                              Ripped coat,
Bad nerves—he took it all in stride.

He cursed eloquently mother, God, and wife.
He put it all together, some snow-brilliant way,
Clichés and all—divined bad breath, general stutter,
Cough—and caught it all suddenly
In amaranth and rhythm, and walked home
Straighter than he could.

I.

The last peacock has lost this feather.
It is, besides dark amber, a reminder
Of the underlayers of serpentine.

On earth there are so many peacocks,
And every feather holding half of what
The senses are. And more: below,

The streams of cochineal, the fishless
Eyes of green, the greedy
Turquoise mouths that never tasted food.

II.

Besides in form, there is a textbook
In the aesthetics of all that ever was,
And all that never shall be seen . . .
In this diamond's reflection.

If this were the last peacock's last feather,
It would last longer than the mouth
Of any moth, and would shine brighter
Than the eye of any human mind.

My gift is gaining. Call it paradox.
The thing I do not have, a yellow bird,
I gladly give and gain it.
I take it from a purple tree
With purple boughs and leaves.

Or take it from some oak so ordinary,
Slanting towards the street,
Not even birds remember it,
Not even birds with bleached brown wings.

But gained I give it up,
Because the yellow bird was there
And what I give I gain.

—after reading Weldon Kees

Most of us spend most of our lives
Climbing in and out of wombs,
Bitching about bad coffee and too wet
Martinis. Most of us lust for, more than love,
Our wives, waitresses, and celluloid sirens.

But a few seem to move to the total horror
Of ennui, to wake tired at morning,
To be glad to face another alley, rather
Than to go on for another hour with the sheets,
Fighting the nightmares that gang up.

Those few are real and positive. They know
What misery and terror really are.
They're usually the very last ones to bitch.
They go off somewhere to drink in a bar
Or cry or quietly to kill themselves.

Prick your finger with a pin
Sharpened thin,
Let blood drip down and splatter
On a clean white plate.
Then with the blood and a goose's feather
Write out your hate
On a rag of paper,
Dream about it,
Sit
With your thumbs gouged in your eyes.
Think of a baby's cries
And drop the paper in a pot.
Add one green lizard, one toad frog, two **flies**
To the water bubbling hot
As you can get it.
Then sit.
Hum. Smell the brew. Think of grass-green.
After a while you will shudder and be clean.

She told me that in the Philippines,
As they all sat on the veranda,
Bats would come up in hordes—
Small-bodied bats with great wing-spread—
Like clouds of rain.

While they all sat, she said,
With their bamboo glasses
And smelled the beginnings of evening,
They remarked the bats only an instant
Between the casual gossip.

Now, she said, those miles away
And years away, she remembered the bats
But none of the talk,
Not one living soul!
Except a young man, exceedingly drunk,
Who told her bats were important.

Poor Hogan wept so wearily
At everything's transparency:
Hearts and lovers, pretty faces,
All that cruel Time erases;

But Hogan wept more wearily
At his own transparency:
No heart, no love, no pretty face,
Nothing at all Time could erase.

III

Oenone, flowers at the burial
Ease tears: the wounded earth is helped to sleep.
But deeper down than serpentine, than rocks
That mark us passionate, down lava-deep

Is grief so harsh that all the amaranth
Comes ciphered to a harshly wrong perfume.
Where all that mates in mock Elysian Fields
Is hate, and hate is final in each bloom.

No Paris can revive the Spring. No turn
Of hand wrought delicate can move away
The pride that Helen squanders with a smile.
The dry-teared hate must well, and it must stay.

Penelope dear, arranging at your phone
The lineaments of all tomorrow's speech,
What else is there, with your Ulysses gone?
A lady has her female right to preach.

The young are wild as ever in the trees,
Breaking the limbs, upsetting evening talk.
And your Ulysses rides across the seas.
What could a proper lady do but balk?

Balk at the sun too hot, the wind too strong—
While holding passion down beneath your eyes—
And, smiling, say Ulysses wasn't wrong
To leave again and search some further skies.

Penelope dear, speak harshly of the man
Who passes by to court your neighbor's wife;
You've done your best too long, and no one can
Stay pure in flesh—and spirit too—for life.

He sits cross-legged, like an ascetic Buddha.
A forgotten eye rests on His hairy lap,
And two claw-hands swim out at the no-color sky.
Below, far down below the rutted hill,
His one eye sees dark Greeks drinking their wine.
A plaited rope of vine joins them together
In their singing and their prayers to Him.
A senile vision, this—His half mind says.

Beside Him lies a broken thunderbolt,
Behind Him dry Olympian char and dust.
His cool Olympian home has died in flames—
And all His women, mortal and immortal.
Elysium itself has turned to wind
And Zeus the God, to unread history.

IV

POEM TO MYSELF, FROM AN ORDINARY SCENE

The scene from a window may excite a guilt,
Snow and smoke together towards the street.
In a warm room sometimes the cold is a quilt
To ease whatever wrong and help repeat
The wrong. Today, my novel put aside,
Another man's adventure gives no calm,
For I have hurt my brother, even tried
His heart. His bleeding wound is in my palm.

TO MY GODSON

Now I am named a father to this child
The stars are not so easy to accept:
Each foot of night blue heaven is a wild
Presentiment; the blazing moon, once kept
Romantic by the sonneteer, is gray,
Deep-pocked—an impotent, unlovely child
Of Earth and Sun. This other child, my son,
Has made me look too close: the natural way
To look again with half-shut eyes. The one
Course left for me is by the harsher say
Of reason, so that I may see each thing
For its sad worth, and those few lovely joys.
And so that I may teach myself to sing
Instructive songs, and give instructive toys.

The strong blue eye, the blood, the bone beneath
    the skin,
The old empowering, the truce of kin
Are least of father now and least towards this
    son's love.
The servant-son, turned free, has turned to love.

He turns from old obedience to refine the state
That nature sets and son accepts, the late
And wise empowering. This new, aggressive love
Is father's dictate and will match his love.

Greatness tends to slink
In times of stress,
And men grow cold
Within the moment waited for.
The hour of dawn is always less
Than what it seemed to be before.

Children see
Heroic fathers pale,
And mothers sometimes leave
Their babes to burn.

The mind is stern till blinded by its tears.
The eyeless heart cannot endure its years.

Gray-feathered birds are nesting in my brain.
The flesh is tender but the pain
Diminutive, for pain is an opiate
For pain.
      But when the young birds hatch and mate
And more claws tear the dwindling skin,
The drug will dwindle too, so thin
That I'll lie powerless, and long
Remain the meaning of their mating-song.

From the pier I fish with worms, finally with bread;
Usually a blue-gill jerks the bait, but sometimes
A bream. A baby snapping-turtle's head
Emerges, eyes bewildered, though he seems
Content to have the hook caught in his throat.
I cut the line, throw turtle and hook, now one,
Into the tricky water floating my boat.
The splash quietens, receiving early sun.

The river's facade of ripples, liquid sun,
The incalculable sound of the small blue boat
Sloshing—all of these gather as one
To feed my five unmighty senses. Throat
Is hard with lump, and what-is only seems
To be: rusty cans, soft mud, fierce glass, the head
Of a woman, eaten by fish. But thank God!
    sometimes
The devil forces through starvation his coarse black
    bread.

Much of my anguish has been
Purposeless but pure:
I never sin
In a high-brow Catholic way
But to the chords of a Methodist preacher's pure
Squealing shout at the devil.

My guilt flares up at every natural evil
I suffer: a girl's bad breath,
A spastic hand, any kind of death.
Electric shock or insulin
Might deaden my guilt, but who is there to pray
For all the silly people lately
In pain—whom I drink for and whom I hate.

TO A CHILD

Little girl
I see your wisdom
What it is
Inspection freshly
Of the changing grass

And here within
Tired skin
My sameness with each tree
Congratulate you morning
With a smile

I am not yoked to
Madness death
Or even children
In my wondering
Or in my sadness, still

I must admire
Each way of looking
Once again
Towards some more green
Less final thing

Before I knew my soul
I knew my father's voice,
The sacrosanct control
Of every final choice
And first. The morning bird
Sang right or wrong for me
By what my father heard.
Through his blue eyes I'd see
The mare and judge her gait.
Somehow from him there grew
My mordant soul—with hate
And fear enough for two.

At the age of thirty
I found fewer defensive walls.

Insecticide had killed the locusts
But where were the trees?
Where was the grass?

One drink was my undoing.
When the others at the party
Came to ice a drink
And said, "What are you doing out here?"
I studied the kitchen sink
And said I didn't know.

The year that I was thirty
All this happened.
I called it my time of *angst*.

Time has blooded my passionate youth,
My clean despair.
The rebel-view from where I stood
Is thick with trees,
Full of the locust sound.
And as for walls, they loom up everywhere.

Like tributaries to small rivers, this
Is love: where the shade is sweet
With ferns, where the clear creek
Seizes up a moment. Frail clover flowers
Join the damp of earth, and gray birds
Circle underneath a camp of water oaks—
Here fierce as Lethe reigns the monster,
Here the monster rages. A day, a moment,
Rotten, sweet, with tree limbs crumbling
Underwards, and a carpet softens underneath
The foot. By water's edge the ferns will droop
In heat or cold; they will not be transplanted.

> *. . . you and I cannot be confined within the weak*
> *list of a country's fashion . . .*

There are many of those sweet unconquerable
    things I
Seize to my heart (although sometimes against
The no-nods of my head). But the eye who faints
Unchallengingly at pigeons, ivy, steep hills,
Boys taking corners on too-giddy wheels,
Or anything that glisters of the profane,
The anti-law—this eye faints against my grain.

The rebel baked in the sun has charm, of course;
Back-grounded by wild growth he sits his horse
With daring ease, saying "Rear, if you please."
He's better than the pallid man, horse-shy,
Who stutters and can't look you in the eye.
Either extreme I find extraneous
(When I have time to think), but most of us
Are nullified by youth and whim, bright wings
That can't be still, most anything that sings
In color with abandon. Strap me to
A tree; use a gag: my mind seeps through
Now and then, just drop by drop—but clear,
I throw an Aristotle blanket where
High glamor breeds. Bruises, sores, analysts
Wait for the whir-dry wings before paralysis.
Death, good sir, frocked well, may be chic
Just now but wait (the mind waits), for a week.

*The glory of young men is their strength: and
the beauty of old men is the gray head.*

Confused as Abelard,
Castrated and in love,
I lay cross-shape on our front yard
And watched the oaks.
Worlds happened in my body.
I cried dry salt; I was blind to flowers.
I spent my days lying down, drinking Cokes
And hunting for girly shots in magazines.

It always took the sun a year to make its arc.
Verbena turned anemic, ferns fell flat;
Motorcycles kept the pavement squealing.
My mind was lichen, tousled—
To me as to my father. Summer moved
Slower than winter, winter than summer.

Everything seemed to be dying
While hair grew on my body.
An alien talked in my throat, my legs were aching.
Dreams I couldn't repeat
Were well worth dreaming.

Vaguely I was a hero:
A football to my chest,
Ape-goggles to my eyes,
A bronzed man moving slow

To the cries of big-bosomed girls.
Vaguely I watched them crucify my weeping father.

Obscene to look upon,
Ugly-smelling of growth,
Narcissistic, nude,
I moved to the thought of windy skirts,
Sparrow-love, careening cars.
Emotionless as an animal.

I moved in mind
But neither moon nor movie star
Could budge the rib-bars under the skinny flesh,
The too-long arms
I tried to hide.

Though I was gross and dying
The grass would cling to my shirt
(And I could not be chooser).
Belly-down—the summer clock stopped—
I moved to the sound of lava,
Dead-slow to the sound of dying.

That hooded day, that day I hated so
When I was a child, and hate today as I grow
Gray hair—Sunday, maudlin-rich with noon:
Just after the preacher's pitch, and too soon
After late breakfast with the bleeding comic
Strips, front page politicians licking
Their lips before carving up the world some more.

Then: Mahogany-red ripe ham (pineapple crusted),
Oyster en casserole, asparagus dusted
Lightly with strong cheese, effete dessert;
Groggy nap; country drive; girl-orchestra concert
From the big box-shaped radio.

                                     Although
I smoke three packs of cigarettes, read trash,
Sit through (bored by) a picture show, salve down
My senses any way I can, don't shave,
Don't dress particularly, behave
Like a bored, befuddled child running to crime,
Sunday's the same devout, dyspeptic time
As before. Its colors reduce to brown.
I've grown eccentric. Sometimes when a knock
Cracks on the door, I ignore it, rock
Right on. My phone was taken out two years
Ago; silence is good for my ears.

Tantalus-like, I bite at the fuzzy peach;
The branch swings up, dangles it out of my reach.

45

And the water recedes when I bow my head. I dread
False teeth. I dread a grizzled mixed-up head.
I steep my hair in barber's potion, wince
At the shaving-mirror's merciless offense.
I wouldn't be nineteen in any sense.

Sunday has multiplied. Someone has fed
It sexing pills. That brackish day has bred
Six ugly children—and each one I dread.

A narrow world to a stranger's eyes, and to mine:
Expanse of wrinkled sheets, impassioned breath
(Somehow the bedroom ended here, and fine
Enough; the rented furnishings were sad),
The weary living room, quiet for death,
Except sometimes we played a hot, mad
Record and cavorted in the skin.
Add bathroom, kitchen; all of the world we were in.

Narrow, yes. But wide enough, and full
(Of vulgar lamps, wall paper pushing in)
Of Empire high romance, sweet sounds made small;
And we were what we were and where we met.
Reason was an alien, and sin
Somebody we forgot we ever met.
Amoral as two pigeons with shut eyes,
We swallowed poppy seeds to grow our lies.

The quiet voice—no louder than before—
That played like hands over a man's bare chest,
The voice went scratching on the skin, even more
Than had it not touched love off in the dark.
No queen were you, no king was I, the rest,
Our world, went gray as the windows and just as
          stark.
We began to dress, stood in our underwear,
Asked "Who are you? gracious not to stare."

V

My mother's border grew on a clean dirt mound;
No weeds undid its pure formality.
Some years dark blood verbena laced and wound
Among itself, but never wild, never free.
Whatever flower stood on guard, it found
A raging land of colors there, a sea
Of grass the other way. Boys turned around,
They might expect some instant laxity
On the border's part: purple asters now unbound,
White rose petals shattering mutinously.
And boys might never know a woman's hands
Work always early mornings, pulling weeds.
The woman, with wet shears, who understands
What ruthless care the clean and formal needs.

There are peripheries of excellence,
Small towns where crafty robbers never chance
A bank, but also where no buildings tower
Breathlessly out of the street. Yet there is power.
And ladies who have not had princes to tea,
Have lived completely out of mystery
But are mysterious as they declare
Their views on table manners, babies, war.
And lovers bounding on back seats of cars,
Crude, unlovely, talking clichés about stars;
These, too, know heightened minutes just before
The muscles ease, then say What else? What more?

Practiced elegance frames up the ease
for meeting nearly anyone, and pleas-
ing him—in overalls or otherwise.
Our good rich friend worked such polite disguise
when buying bulls from a farmer, the farmer said:
"Lady, you're common as dirt." The lady was glad.
She'd passed the something line without offense.
The farmer chewed and spat and wasn't tense.

But practiced elegance halts short,
the way of a mare whose filmy eyes distort
the truth of distance. Learn high fashion all
you please, dear ladies, from the *Bazaar*, and call
your aces from Miss Rowland's School.
But a vulgar man's no fool.
Like a prowling animal he prowls by smell
and understands true elegance quite well.

By "practiced elegance halts short" I mean
it's not enough to make the farmer's spleen
die down in front of wealth. If he's not good
and works by stealth, he can jerk the cosmetic hood
right off, no matter how much money paid
to Helena Rubinstein. His sword is made
of being what he is, and that could be
most anything uncouth, and hatefully.

All this is common knowledge you can find
in any almanac of facts. But the blind

53

are abundant as ever, gnawing on pretense
like a bone, and never dreaming there is sense—
or being civilized, is better—to
it all. Most of the Ladies I once knew
are dead. My Mother was one, and though well-bred,
being a lady never entered her head.

At table, feet must be flat on the floor.
Don't cross your legs. If something's spilled, ignore
It. Spread your napkin out, first thing, across
Your lap. Eat some of all. It's *your* loss
If you don't. Why once I couldn't eat
An oyster raw, and now—what a treat!
Don't fidget when your uncle says long blessing;
He means it all. Besides, he's always stressing
You to God. You should be glad you've got
So many relatives who care a lot
About you. When you've finished eating and
Must go, excuse yourself before you stand.
This is how a gentleman should act.
It's manners now but later will be tact.

So spoke my Mother, many and many a time,
These words, adultly, only not with rhyme,
And guiltily I sit today, to eat,
Not minding my napkin right or my truant feet,
But nevertheless I *know*, as I used to know
What was sin and, where the comma should go.

HOUSECLEANING

The usually staid, comfortable rooms—
Decked with antiques not too old or too extreme—
Metamorphosed suddenly into
The dislocated setting of a dream.
Beyond stacked furniture I saw the blooms
Of roses—"Sutter's Gold" and "Peace"—all new
Because the slightest sign of crinkling death
On a rose's skin, brought out sharp scissors fast.
The roses were arranged and rooted, staid.
Around me was the awful price you paid
For being decently clean and in good health.
I had a feeling the temporal would last:
Those brand new roses waving to the past.

                         Soon I would be—
Unhandsome child of seventeen and marked
With pimples and post graduate
Adolescence; I no longer ate
Sweets; everything embarrassed me—
I would be quiet and hidden somewhere,
Behind an over-turned, over-stuffed, chintz-covered
    chair
Or in the garden behind the fortress of hedge.
I knew I lived just then on a crumbling ledge
Though beside me marigolds bloomed and grass
        was green—
And smooth, halcyon buzzing came from unseen
Creatures camouflaged in the summer green.

After a week or so, the house would flow
Back into normal. A Victorian chair might be
Exiled to garage—at first, jarringly—
But a week would make it seem true alien there.
"How was there ever room for another chair?"

The fleeting smell of turpentine, the panes
Sparkling sun, the beds too clean, almost,
For a sweating animal to touch—the cost
(I didn't pay) was worth these royal gains.

I took a bath each night for a solid week,
Tried not to think of my squalid college rooms
(Dirty shorts on the floor, stacked books, one ceiling-
      leak)
But, gathering spoils not mine, and offensively meek,
I, rocking and clean, looked out at the "Sutter's"
      blooms.

BACK HOME, AND READING

This was a summer day so hot the flies
Did tail-spins in mid-flight.
Porch ferns were limp as peacock feathers pulled.
People drank Cokes and waited for night.

Convincing myself of a harbor past all this—
Siberian cool but nice—
I rocked in a wicker chair on our front porch,
Read books and ate a glass of ice.

The books—I'd just run out of ones I'd brought—
Were Bryan's speeches and
The like, that punctured hearts some years ago.
But how, I couldn't understand.

Then I remembered something on my bed—
A yellow magazine
Of exposé. A writer said some duke
My Mother liked had been "obscene."

Or worse. The hint was that he'd been much worse.
I left my wicker place
To find a son's foul reading on chenille.
Relieved, I saw no wrinkled trace

That the magazine had moved. I burned it up.
Not only would she grieve
About her duke, but understand a third.
I wanted her at least two-thirds naive.

Two years ago, counting back from January. . .
In Alabama a kind of wintry, wary
Spring had begun. Next month camellias would
    open,
In March the jonquils, then anything could happen
As far as flowers were concerned. You yearned
For them that spring, I know it, Mother,
Lying on patched hospital sheets, smothering
(Cold, cooped up) in a dinky room, its walls
Tranquility-gray. You lay there, a hand-knitted
    shawl,
The color of honey, around your shoulders;
It was wintry in Alabama, ever colder
As camellias budded and suddently burst.
Though icy, this was the warmest of the worst
Three winters you knew. Your flowers were worked
    by the man
(He talked to himself; so what?) you used to stand
Over at seventy-five cents an hour. Many years,
Many words taught him the art of hoe and shears.

Easter, I wasn't aware of the "ritual story"—
Nothing new to wear, broke, playing with the glory
Of being mortal. Tons of Greyhound bus
Moaned through the wind, coldly delivering us
To wedding beds, fresh wars, new griefs.
I studied the faces around me, sleeping and brief.
I read in a smutty newspaper that emotion

59

Could now be applied like a facial lotion.
New Year! cut the adder's head in two!
I'm poisoned with fear. I'm poisoned with love too.

                                        Summer scolds
The yard today; verbena droops; blind moles
Cave through the earth, leaving line-mounds of
    lawn.
I, incompetent as ever, am drawn
Back to your winter days. Rich fawning ferns
Remind me they need water. The sky burns.

The lawn was cut, but thorny weeds bloomed by
The red verbena. We had a sunny sky.

The women had forsaken me: sister,
Aunts and cousins, hidden back somewhere
To weep, to whisper, to see that coffee perked.
"Not-there," stranger-at-home, I fairly lurked
On our front porch, the rouge-tile freshly mopped.
That was Cousin Abram? The one who chopped
His finger off, on a bet? "This one who chopped
His finger off is Cousin Abram; this is . . ."
Ill-dressed in a tight, stained skirt, she said, "Mrs.
Crantenwell," blew smoke, "I used to rent
From y'Mother. Five years or more. They sent
The corpse?" Her ankles were dirty and her legs
Could have used a shave. Poor woman was town-
        dregs.
Men said beef prices would go up in the fall.
Their children on the lawn played mock baseball.

I tried to sleep out the wake. Men mumbled past
My door. Cups clinked.
                                        You poor outcast
(But no more than I) lay on the too-soft bed,
White-satin finished.
                                        Darling vacant-head,
Cosmeticked for the town to see, ignore
The muted chaos, pink eyelids, be bored.

Delighted by, made her delightful;
Conversation flew.
Tea roses made her face go smiling.
This is all she knew:
Porch talk is made for happy listening
(Sorrow we eschew),
And roses made for much admiring.
This is what she knew.

STORIES

The Hitch-Hiker

Then while time serves, and we are but decaying,
Come, my Corinna, come let's go a-Maying.

"How far are you going?" I said. I had caught a
glimpse of his eyes; they were pale blue.

"To Shady Springs," he said. He sat, with his hands
knotted in his lap, and looked away from me, out the
window of the car. He wouldn't be much to talk, I told
myself, and I saw, at the bottom of his denim pants,
brogans coated with dry mud. He must have been working in the fields that day, or some days earlier, I thought.

The Johnson Pike, between Red Bay and Shady
Springs, is lined with pines and oaks. There are occasional
breaks, where the landscape shows through, and you
can see cultivated fields of cotton and corn, fields that
haven't been touched for fifty years or more, and now
and then bright green pastures studded with cattle. But
I felt that he was not looking at the trees, or anything
outside the car; he was thinking, and I knew he wouldn't
be much to talk.

It was five miles outside Red Bay that I picked him
up. He was standing, in the first place, on the wrong side
of the road, with his fist and pointed thumb barely raised.
He stood in front of a Chesterfield sign nailed to a big
oak, and there weren't any houses for at least a mile in
any direction.

I don't usually pick up hitch-hikers, I'm against it
in principle, but there was something about the way he
slumped, almost cowered, in front of the signboard with
the woman blowing smoke rings, something too about
the way he almost grudgingly lifted his fist and pointed
thumb when he heard my car and never bothered to look

up until I had stopped. I don't know why I stopped, but I believe I felt that I somehow should. I could not have seen the strange pale eyes before he got in the car; I remember for a fact exactly when I saw them.

About two miles from where I picked him up, near where Stuart's Mill used to be, the hitch-hiker turned from the window and began to work through his pockets for a cigarette. There was an opened pack on the dashboard, and I offered him one.

"Maybe they're stale," I said. "I don't smoke as a rule, only sometimes when there's a long stretch of driving."

"They're fine." He turned back to the window and dipped the cigarette out into the rushing air.

Offering him the cigarette hadn't worked, I thought; he just wouldn't talk. But before it had gone completely through my mind, he had moved quickly and smoothly, so that his back was to the door and he squarely faced my right side. I realized immediately that his movement was too sudden and too perfected to be natural, but it was not for some seconds that I saw, from the corner of my eye, the blade of a long knife held tight in his fist and rested on his knee.

I thought first of stopping the car, then of my stupidity for having picked him up, but I kept driving at the same speed. He'd have to speak soon or later, I told myself, and I waited.

But before he spoke, he began to hum, and I thought, as I listened to him and tried to make out what the tune was, that he must be smiling. The music was not in any way mean or bitter, and for an instant I forgot about the knife that rested on his knee, and I followed the tune.

Because of the lines of trees along Johnson Pike, it gets dark early; and far ahead I saw two beams of headlights, and I automatically snapped on mine. Then the humming stopped, and I felt the point of the knife on my shoulder.

"Keep right on," he said. "Don't stop."

His voice sounded exactly the same as when he first got in the car—detached, as if the words fell out of his mouth and somehow fell in the right order.

That was all he said, and he lowered the knife to my ribs, just below the arm pit. The car lights ahead of us grew and grew until we were finally showered with light and I could see his faded clothes and a blur of part of his face reflected in the windshield. Then the car was gone, and he rested the knife again on his knee.

"Do you know this road?" he said.

I nodded.

"Stop when you come to the Old Coates Bridge. It ain't far ahead. Stop just this side of it."

The trees were great shaggy splotches that let in brief patches of the darkening sky. Johnson Pike seemed no different, I felt, from the way it had seemed at least a hundred times before, but it was different, I felt I had to insist, and I was not being fair with myself nor with the situation not to admit it.

I had to think of exactly the right words, not too many words so as to make a fool of myself, and not too few so as to seem disturbed, but the right amount—the words he might say, and the way he might say them. Words, too, that were precise, just as the knife that rested on his knee.

"Do you want money, or the car? What is it you want?"

It was the way I might have said, do you take cream in your coffee? or black?

I did not see him move, but he did, for I saw his knee, perfectly still, and the knife was no longer there.

"I want both," he said. "Your money and the car. All you've got."

He leaned forward and looked through the windshield.

"It's not far," he said. "Remember, stop just this side of it. Or if you see a woman before then, go slow. I'm supposed to meet a woman."

I wondered how the woman would look, and felt that her eyes must surely be pale and blue, and that she would stand cowering in front of a Chesterfield sign. I could not remember how the hitch-hiker's face looked, only the eyes, and I began to construct the rest around them. The cheeks and forehead would be high, the face long and burned by the sun, the lips thin . . .

"Over the hill yonder is the bridge. Drive slower."

We were at the bottom of the hill, beside a sign that advertised the Drake Hotel in Shady Springs, then past the sign, and making our way towards an early sprinkling of evening stars. The lines of trees climbed with us, but we seemed less shut in now that the wide sky lay beyond the windshield. The sky was much darker than his eyes.

From the top of the hill, I could see, far to the left, the lights of Shady Springs, and at the bottom of the hill, almost absorbed in darkness, the white concrete bridge.

"Slow down, dammit!" The wind caught parts of the words, for he had turned, and his head was out the window. "She may be along here somewhere."

It was the first time the words had not seemed to fall and to find their own order; they were not detached, but frantic, and they insisted on obedience.

"You look on that side." For an instant his head was back inside the car, and his hand, gripping the knife, lay on the dashboard. "You look close, and if you see a woman, sing out. Hear me, sing out."

He may have said more that was lost, for his head was suddenly out the window again.

I began to look for a Chesterfield sign, knowing that she would stand in front of it, cowering, held to her place by the lights of the car. What if her eyes were brown? but he'd not claim her then, I thought.

The bridge was just ahead, ten or fifteen feet, and there was still no signboard and no woman, but some distance on the other side of the bridge, and to the left of the road, I could see the back side of a signboard.

"Stop," he said. "Pull off the road, into that clump of trees yonder."

He got out of the car first, and came around to my side and opened the door. The knife was still in his hand, and the blade caught a little light from the early stars.

"Get out," he said.

The cheeks and forehead were high, or perhaps they seemed so because I was looking up at him, and his face was long, but I could not tell if it were burned by the sun. Had I left the head-lights on, I might have been sure. But I could tell only that his face was long, and that he was taller than I had thought.

"Where was she to meet you?" I said.

"Here. Right here at this bridge. She was going to wait for me."

"When?" I said. "When were you to meet her?"

"She was going to wait till I came, and she ain't here. She didn't come."

His words had begun to fall again, casually, perfectly placing themselves.

"Sound the horn. She ain't here, but sound it anyway."

I leaned inside the car and pushed the palm of my hand against the round cool metal. The noise was dull and low, and not like it had ever sounded before.

69

"That's enough. We don't want to raise the dead. She ain't here, and I won't wait any longer. She said she would be, though. She said this morning she'd be right here at this bridge."

"See that sign," I said. I pointed to the other side of the bridge. "Maybe she's there."

I felt foolish after I had said it, and I wondered if he understood what I meant.

"She was to be at this bridge," he said, "not at that billboard. She didn't come."

"We could look. It wouldn't hurt to look. You wouldn't want to miss her."

My words were childish and begging, not at all like his.

"It was to be here, right here at this bridge. Anyway, if she was over there, she could hear us."

"But it wouldn't be right not to look, not after you've got this far, and taken chances." I felt I had to make him understand, but there was no way to explain it.

"You look," he said. "She's not there, but if you want to, look. I'll wait right here."

As I crossed the bridge, I could see the stream gleaming below me, and I wondered why I could not remember the sign, for I knew Johnson Pike by heart. But before I got there, I knew the sign was not a Chesterfield advertisement. I could see in my mind the letters painted large and black against a bright yellow background: NEHI, and there was a picture of a woman with her dress lifted to her knees.

I turned back, and I could not bear the thought of telling him. I had been so positive, I had known she would be there, and now, even worse than not finding her, was telling him.

When I returned to the car, he was gone. I decided to sit down and wait, but before I had opened the car door, I heard him running through the thicket along the side of the stream. I ran to the bridge and leaned over the water.

"She wasn't there," I shouted. "It was a Nehi sign."

He didn't answer, and then I couldn't hear him any more.

"I won't report you," I shouted, and I don't think he heard me, but it didn't make any difference, I knew, for he wouldn't have cared if I did.

Suffer the Little Children

Marier drank paregoric, and she was a wonder of my young life. Ten years ago while I was in college I read about her death, and at that time the short notice on the back page of the Taylor City *Examiner* did not much move me. The death was too remote to seem real, and not till I went back the following summer to Taylor City and smelled the heat rising up from the sidewalks and watched the farmers gathered in the square, wearing their faded overalls, and their wives in flour-sack dresses, did Marier's death come real to me.

Marier was about four feet tall, and she lived with Old Patrick, the street cleaner. About the time you saw her coming down the street, you could smell the paregoric she had been drinking, and the odor—especially on a hot, close summer day—always would make your stomach feel uneasy.

I was afraid of her when I was very young. Her face was shrivelled; and she wore old clothes too big for her, and tied her feet up in grain sacks. Marier talked to herself in a way that made you feel someone was there you couldn't see.

But I came to accept Marier when I was a little older. I think I was ten. I came to accept her and lose my fear because I saw her afraid and humiliated.

One afternoon some of the older boys—I'm sure the Heston twins were among them—waited with a dead, green snake behind a corner at the York Hardware Store. When Marier passed, they dangled the snake before her, then chased her with it as she ran the best she could, and screamed. While I watched them running down the street —Marier pathetic with those clumsy sacks around her feet

—I laughed because all the other boys were laughing, and then later I pitied her and felt ashamed of myself. But I was not afraid anymore.

The next fall I took a morning paper route. Dawn would find me squatting beside my bicycle, folding copies of the *Examiner* in front of the Greyhound Bus Station. I'd watch Marier's man, Old Patrick, come up through gray-pearl light from South Taylor City, a long-handled broom over his shoulder, and at his side Marier pushing a cart into which went rubbish from the streets. Marier would stop and talk to me while I folded papers and Old Patrick would go on about his cleaning.

"Whose boy are you?" she'd say.

"Mr. Hamilton's," I'd answer, and maybe a week from then she'd ask me the same question.

"What do they call you?"

"Tom."

"Tom, you're a nice boy," Marier would tell me. "I know your daddy. He's a nice man." She'd pronounce my name Tawm.

Usually she'd leave pretty soon to start cleaning the Taylor City Grocery before it opened, but sometimes she'd stay long enough to tell me about the rheumatism in her back or to look at a newspaper which she could not read.

A couple of months after I started the route, she first asked me for money. Old Patrick was still in the distance, ready to turn the corner to the court house, and Marier had waited until I was almost through folding my papers.

"I reckon you make lots of money with these here papers," she said, tapping one against the basket of my bicycle.

I told her it wasn't much and I was saving up to go to Mammoth Cave with the Boy Scouts next summer.

"Couldn't you loan old Marier a quarter for some breakfast bacon? I'll pay you on Saturday when I get paid."

I didn't know how to answer that I couldn't, and so I took a quarter from my pocket.

"You're the sweetest boy," she said. "You're the sweetest boy, and old Marier's gonna always love you."

She hugged my neck, and the paregoric odor was terrible to my empty stomach. After she had gone, I wanted my quarter back, but I knew I wouldn't get it Saturday or ever, because she would buy paregoric with it, and when that paregoric was gone, she'd be looking for another quarter.

The next morning she met me again. She asked for another quarter and I gave it to her. This went on into the next week, till Friday, a quarter a morning, and I began to feel I'd be working all my life just to buy Marier paregoric.

When Friday came and I had only fifty cents for my father to deposit in the bank, he wanted to know where the paper money had gone.

"You started to buy cigarettes?" he said.

"No sir."

"What have you been doing with the money then?"

"I can't tell you," I said.

I turned away from him and lay down on the bed, my face against the balls of cotton on the bedspread.

He spoke gently: "Tell me."

Then when I did, he turned me over on the bed.

"You know what she does with that money?" he said. "She buys paregoric and stays drunk on it. That's what she does with them quarters you give her."

"I know," I said.

Father left the room. I think he was as much at a loss as I had been when Marier asked me for money.

That night at supper my Mother and Father sat silent. Finally I had to speak.

"You won't say nothing to Marier, will you, Papa?"

He didn't answer me but lifted another fork of food.

"Please don't say nothing, Papa," I said, and then I began to cry.

Mother took me to my room and left me there in the darkness. After a while, Father came and sat with me.

"You don't give her no more of your money. Hear me?" He said it sternly, but I knew he was trying to be kind.

"I won't give her any more money," I said, "but don't tell her. You promise?"

He promised me he wouldn't.

I lay awake a long time that night, wondering what I would say to Marier next morning when she asked me for a quarter. When I got up and went to get the papers, I still didn't know what I'd say.

When Marier came up from South Taylor City through the strange morning light, pushing the cart a few feet behind Old Patrick, she looked like a sad scarecrow learning to walk. I wouldn't look up at her when she stood beside me and talked about the pains in her hip. I kept my eyes down on the papers, folding, and trying not to cry.

"You gonna give old Marier a quarter this morning to buy her some collard greens?"

Once she asked, it was no trouble for me to look up at her, my eyes dry now, and to stare into her shrivelled face.

"No. You can't have no money. I don't want you coming around here and bothering me no more. You go on, now. You ought to be ashamed asking little boys for money to buy that paregoric. Go on."

Then I went to the gutter, picked up a stone as large as my fist, and held it back to throw. Marier left without speaking.

The Prisoner

The train roared past the Oklahoma countryside—silent-looking space with hard sun.

Pfc. Forbes and the prisoner held a crossword puzzle book between them, supporting it on their knees. Both of them wore Army uniforms, and both had a pencil in hand.

"What starts with S, has five letters, and means sugar?" the prisoner asked. He bit the end of his pencil and looked—eyes blank—through the windowpane.

"I can't think of that now. I'm on another one," Forbes said.

Forbes was thin, he had a gaunt face, and he looked to be about twenty-three years old. He wore his khakis neatly; the creases in his pants came to a sharp edge. A thin coat of dust lay over the toes of his low-cuts, but a handkerchief could easily have made them glisten. There was a .45 strapped around his waist.

"These things are stupid!" Forbes said. "I mean *stu*pid. No sense to them." He looked at the prisoner beside him. "How could *agreeable* mean *well-liked*? It doesn't. These things must be made for morons. Like me." He pointed to the squares where he had printed *agreeable*. "See," he said, *"agreeable!"*

The prisoner nodded. His build was thick, and black, crew-cut hair grew over a face which looked its age: some twenty years. His khakis were wrinkled and very dirty.

Five seats behind them sat a sergeant, even more starched than Forbes. His whole countenance seemed starched. On the seat beside him there was a neat stack of magazines; he thumbed through *Look*, reading nothing, not even the captions under the pictures. His pale face was prudish, almost ascetic, and a small scar on his upper lip furthered this. Now and then he looked at Forbes and the prisoner, but for only a second.

"Let's put this thing away," Forbes said. "I guess it's good for that."

Forbes put the pencil in his shirt pocket, stretched both his arms forward, and settled back. His hand shifted the .45 and then settled in his lap.

"Christ, that was a hole back there," he said. "That stockade. What a *hole*. I'd rather be fighting the Russians."

"It ain't no fun. This here is my second time." Then after a pause, "I got in a fight the other time."

"How long you been there? I mean how long at *that* stockade," Forbes said.

"Week, ten days. Let's see: eight days. That don't count though. On my time. That was just till you and the sergeant come to get me. My time'll start after I get back to Polk when they sentence me."

"That bastard," Forbes said. "The sergeant, I mean. He's stewin' back there. You know what he wanted to do? He planned all this on the way up. He was gonna sit right beside you, handcuffed to you, and I was supposed to sit across the aisle with my .45 aimed right at your belly. He just wanted to show off in front of all the people."

The prisoner grinned. "You want a cigarette?" he said. "Has the sergeant got much time in the Army?"

"Naw," Forbes said. "I don't want a cigarette. Naw. He hasn't got much time. He came in with the National Guard or something." Forbes clenched his right fist and inspected his fingernails. "And you oughta heard what they told us back at Polk—the MP's—when we started out for you. *This* is a hardened criminal, they said. You gotta be careful. He's rough. Don't hesitate to shoot. And so the sergeant says to me, *I ain't gonna serve that bastard's time. He gets smart, he just lifts an eyebrow wrong, I'm gonna shoot.*" Forbes let out a mock-tired breath. "The sergeant is great."

The prisoner looked at Forbes and grinned. "You're takin' a chance, you know. You heard the sergeant. He said I was your responsibility. Without the handcuffs."

"Okay. Run. I'll shoot you dead." Forbes patted the gun.

"I'll bet."

The two didn't speak for a long time. The prisoner looked out the window and Forbes stared at the ceiling. Finally, after Forbes had dug into his tight khaki pants for a cigarette and then lighted it, he said:

"How come you A-WOL? You go A-WOL it's all right with me, but how come you did?"

The prisoner crossed his legs and folded his hands over his left thigh.

"Well—everybody was goin'. See our outfit—the rest of us, some has already gone—we was waitin' to ship out. They didn't even have roll call and we just set around all day. Ping pong, pool. Half the soldiers went to town— Leesville, Lake Charles. Some all the way to New Orleans. So I said to myself, It ain't far to Oakie City, and I can see the old lady again before we move out. I'll spend about a day there, and then come back and won't nobody know the difference."

"But they did," Forbes said.

"So I got on a Greyhound bus. I wasn't very smart and didn't fix up any leave papers or anything. I just wasn't very smart. It's easy as hell to do.

"So on the Greyhound bus, after we got about twenty miles from Leesville, we picked up this woman standin' on the side of the road. She was about thirty-five, I guess.

Wasn't very good-looking, but she was kinda sexy. So she set down by me. We got to talkin'." The prisoner stopped and scratched his ear lobe. "We got to talkin' and next stop I got off and bought us a pint of whiskey. And so forth. You know."

"Yeah. But how did they get you?" Forbes said. "The MP's."

The prisoner bit at his thumbnail and wiped the end of his tongue with his little finger.

"When we got into the City I got off the bus and said so long to the broad, and I was about to get in a taxi. A cop walked up to the broad and grabbed her by the arm. The cop was there waitin' for her. She didn't pay her hotel bill someplace. I told the taxi driver to gun it, but the cop hollered at him. So there I was. The cop wanted to see my papers."

Forbes turned to look at the sergeant. He held *True Confessions* in front of his face.

"Why'd they stop *you*?" Forbes asked. "It was her they wanted."

"I don't know. They saw me talkin' to her. Anyway, they get a reward if they turn in a A-WOL."

"Bastards," Forbes said.

"Hey, I wanta tell you something." The prisoner pushed back at his crew-cut. "I wanta thank you."

"What the hell for?"

"You know. Back there at Oakie City. Goin' in to get the crossword book for me."

"Hell," Forbes said. "That wasn't anything."

"And bein' responsible for me," the prisoner added. "Keepin' the handcuffs off."

"I just wanted to show up that sergeant. He's plenty mad. You know what he said to me? See, we're in the same outfit. I don't know him much or anything, but we're in the same outfit. So he comes over the other day and says, I got you a good deal. We got a prisoner down near your home, and I put you on orders—me and you. I said, hell I didn't live in Oklahoma, I live in Alabama. I told him I didn't want to chase prisoners anyhow. Somebody might think I was an MP. So the sergeant said maybe it would be fun for me to see how the other half lived. That sergeant's a clown." Forbes paused. "You afraid? Going back to the stockade?"

"Naw. It wasn't too bad before—when I got in the fight. It wasn't no fun. Some of the guards are pretty rotten. But it wasn't too bad."

"I don't envy you," Forbes said. "I'm going to sleep for a while. Don't run off."

He slipped off his shoes, then sank down and closed his eyes. The prisoner opened his crossword puzzle book to a clean page.

Forbes couldn't go to sleep. He kept thinking of the stockade where they picked up the prisoner. He and the sergeant had to wait all morning, then till after chow, for the prisoner to be cleared. Almost three hours, Forbes watched a red-faced boy stand in the hot sun, in the road facing the main office. Forbes asked one of the guards why the boy was standing there, and the guard told him the boy wouldn't work.

"We're waitin' for the old man," the guard said, "to see what the old man wants to do with him."

The red-faced boy, his shoulders slouched, looked at the ground for half an hour and then told the guard he wanted to go to the latrine.

"You stay right there," the guard said. "You say you ain't gonna work, and so you wait right there till the old man gets back."

The boy spat at the yellow dust.

"When's he gonna get back?"

"Dunno."

"Well, I gotta go to the goddam latrine."

The guard didn't answer him.

Forbes tried not to look. There was something too private and embarrassing here for him to be watching. Forbes was almost ashamed as he looked down at his own clean khakis.

Later on, the red-faced boy began to shout, his mouth a great O and his voice shrill with hate. "Hey! Hey! You guard, you! Dammit, I've gotta go to the goddam latrine! You hear me? Lookit me!"

The guard paid no attention.

"You hear me!"

Forbes wanted to walk out to the guard and say, *Now listen, he wants to go to the latrine, so why don't you let him go? That won't hurt anything. It's a man's right to be able to go to the latrine—like a man. No matter if he's killed somebody.* But Forbes didn't say it. Instead, he looked at some orders on the bulletin board.

The sergeant had put away a comic book and was standing at the door, watching.

"Listen to that bastard," he said. Then after a minute, "Hey, look. He's wet hisself."

Forbes looked out the window and saw a dark stain down one leg of the boy's pants. The boy glared up at the sun, and his face was the color of raw meat.

Just before chow, two MP's brought in a handcuffed Negro, one eye shut to, his lips swollen.

"You damn, you damn, you damn, you damn." The Negro almost sang it. His voice was closer to hurt sobbing than to anger.

An MP behind the desk wanted to know what was the trouble.

"He got in a fight," one of his captors said. "Pulled

a knife on a pore civilian boy. Too much of that good juice."

The man behind the desk winked. "I betcha it was over some sweet baby doll. How 'bout it? Was it over some sweet little baby doll?"

The MP's took the Negro's wallet and began to look through the contents.

"Now looka here," one of them said. "Just looka here."

Forbes watched him hold out a photograph, first at arm's length, then just in front of his eyes.

"Hey, mother, where'd you pick up this pretty piece of black stuff?" the MP said.

The other two men looked at the photograph and whistled.

"She could see her daddy-o now," one of them said, "she wouldn't think *he* was so pretty. Them lips too swole for kissin'."

"You damn, you damn," the Negro said. Forbes thought the Negro was crying, but he couldn't see any tears.

"For Chrissake," Forbes whispered. He went to the wash room and thought he would vomit. He washed his face, and when he went back the Negro was gone. Behind the desk the MP filled out papers. The red-faced boy was still waiting for the old man. The sergeant had returned to his comic book.

Forbes watched the sergeant and muttered, just audible, "You stinkin' pig."

The sergeant looked up. "What?" he said.

"I said when we gonna get the hell outa this place?"

But they had to eat chow there, with spoons, because knives and forks weren't allowed in the prisoners' mess hall. A few minutes after one o'clock, Forbes and the sergeant signed for their prisoner and left.

In Shreveport there was an hour and a half wait till their train left for Leesville.

At the Walk-Inn—a dirty place with menus covering the walls—the prisoner sat between Forbes and the sergeant.

"I don't see anything I want," Forbes said. "I guess I'll have a hamburger. What a place to eat." He looked at the prisoner and said, "We could have picked a better place for your last meal."

The prisoner said he wanted a grilled cheese; the sergeant decided on a bowl of chili.

The sergeant put his wallet on the counter and took out some papers.

"It's not here," he said. "I forgot it."

"What?" Forbes asked.

"The damn meal ticket. For the prisoner here."

"What are you gonna do?"

A man in a dirty apron was poised—with pencil and pad—waiting to take their orders.

"Nothin'. Ain't nothin' to do. He'll have to go without."

"Have to go with*out*!" Forbes said. "*You* forgot his meal ticket, for Chrissake. Where it it?"

"On the train."

"You forgot the meal ticket and so this guy's gotta go without."

The sergeant lifted open palms. "He can pay for his own if he wants to. I ain't walkin' back for the goddam meal ticket."

"You got a lovable streak all up and down you." Forbes slammed his water glass down on the counter. "You know he doesn't have any money. Christ!"

The sergeant stretched himself forward, his elbows on the counter. He wore a fake smile.

"Listen," he said. "This here is a *prisoner*, he ain't the King of England, for God's sake. This here is a prisoner who went A-WOL. He ain't a human *being* any more. This is a *prisoner* and it don't matter to me if he eats or if he don't eat. Now you can—"

"Forget it!" Forbes said. Then to the waiter, "He wants a grilled cheese and milk and I want a hamburger and milk. Put 'em both on my ticket."

The sergeant said he wanted a bowl of chili and a Coke, and to put *that* on *his* bill.

Forbes drummed his fingers on the counter. None of them spoke till they were finished eating.

Then Forbes said to the prisoner, "If you want anything else, you say so. I got plenty of money."

The prisoner shook his head.

Forbes said, "Let's go."

Outside the restaurant, the three of them looked in the direction of what seemed to be downtown.

"Wanta take a walk?" Forbes said, not including the sergeant.

"Okay," the prisoner said.

The sergeant followed about twenty feet behind them.

"He gives me the creeps," Forbes said. "I don't know what's the matter with that guy."

"He don't like prisoners."

"He don't like anybody. You need anything? You wanta buy anything? This'll be your last chance."

"Naw." Then after a few steps, "If you could loan me the money—I'll pay you back. All I want is some shaving cream and hair oil."

"Hell, yes, I'll loan it to you," Forbes said.

"I'll have to get the hair stuff in a tube. You can't have nothin' glass in the stockade."

"We'll go by a ten-cent store."

On what seemed to be the main street they saw, about a block away, a Woolworth store. The sidewalk was fairly crowded, and Forbes, looking over his shoulder, saw the sergeant working his way to keep them in sight.

"You know," Forbes said, and thumbed back of them, "I'll bet if the sergeant's dear old mother was a military prisoner that bastard would let her starve to death. If he didn't have her meal ticket."

In Woolworth's, Forbes stopped at the nut counter to buy cashews.

"Where can I get shaving cream and stuff?" the prisoner asked the teen-age clerk.

She told him the other side of the store, at the front.

"I'll meet you over there in a minute," Forbes said and then told the girl he wanted a quarter pound of cashews.

While the girl weighed the nuts, Forbes watched the prisoner making his way across the store. Then his eyes rested on the sergeant, just two counters behind the prisoner, removing the .45 from its holster, then raising it.

"Stop it! Stop it!" Forbes shouted as he ran to the sergeant. His hand came down on the sergeant's arm just as the gun was aimed. The gun fell to the floor without firing.

"You nut!" Forbes said, holding the sergeant by both shoulders. "You crazy, *crazy* nut. He's not running away. He's getting some shaving cream, for Chrissake." He gave the shoulders a push and said, "*Shav*ing cream."

The sergeant didn't speak. There was a crowd gathering around the two men, and when Forbes saw this, he cleared his way to the prisoner.

"What happened?" the prisoner asked.

"Not a thing. Not a damn thing," Forbes said. "Let's get back to the train."

They were twenty minutes out of Shreveport. The sergeant, sitting across the aisle from Forbes and the prisoner, had been talking for the last five minutes. The scar on his lip was unusually white.

". . . and when I do—when I do make out my report, Private Forbes is gonna be in *serious* trouble, I mean *serious* trouble." He took a clean, folded handkerchief and wiped his brow, which had no sweat on it. "Boy, you been foolin' around with Uncle Sam's property—this here prisoner is Uncle Sam's property, he ain't no human being no more—you been—you been—" He stopped and hit his right fist into the palm of his other hand. "I don't know what'll happen to you. I don't care. I ain't gonna be easy on you in my report. You hear that?"

Forbes stared back at him. The prisoner looked down.

"You a college graduate, now ain't you?" the sergeant said. "Yeah, I know you're a college graduate. How come they didn't *teach* you nothin' at that college? Huh? How come they didn't? Huh? Can't you talk or nothin'? Didn't they even teach you how to talk?"

Forbes spoke slowly and just loud enough for the sergeant to hear him. "I kept you from killin' a man awhile ago. You think about that for a minute. This prisoner didn't do a thing and you nearly killed him. You think about that when you write up the report. And don't forget the meal ticket."

The sergeant opened his mouth to answer, but didn't. He went down the aisle to his seat.

"I hope the hell you're not in trouble," the prisoner said. "It was my fault."

"Forget it. And don't talk to me, will you?"

Forbes closed his eyes, and after the anger had begun to settle he knew he had been wrong. The sergeant was wrong and the prisoner was wrong—and he, Forbes, was wrong, too. . . . Things sometimes went that way.

He knew, though, he need not worry about the sergeant's report. There would be no report.

Honest Dirt

One side of the house burst forth with bay windows, the other side eased into front porch. From where she was standing Mrs. Jasper Bailey could see her son, D. B., propped back in a big cane rocker, painted green, and seemingly reading the Birmingham *News*. At least the paper was spread out in front of him; you couldn't see his face.

She worried herself to death about D. B., he was so pale and just sat around all the time. He was about five and a half feet tall, stocky, but his skin was the color of barely-gray milk. Oh she'd tried to get him out in the sun, just to work for a while in her flowers, but he said the sun hurt his eyes—he'd always had trouble with his eyes one way or other but he wouldn't wear glasses— and he said he got blistered too easy. "If you'd wear sun glasses or put a shirt on ever once in a while . . . It just ain't healthy, not according to God's plan," Mrs. Bailey would say, and D. B. would answer, not looking up from his reading, "Healthy schmealthy."

There he was, *she* saw him, flipping cigarette ashes onto the clean front porch she swept that morning—just before Miss Lottie Simpson came, an old maid and Mrs. Bailey's best friend. They told each other everything.

On the porch that morning Mrs. Bailey whispered to Lottie: "Let's go around back. To the garden."

D. B. was sitting barefoot and cleaning his toenails. He wore khaki pants and a sleeveless undershirt.

"Don't whisper on my account," D. B. said. His voice was early-morning hoarse. "I ain't interested."

"D. B., how could you *say* such a thing?" Mrs. Bailey

whimpered. Then in her normal voice to Lottie, "Come on," and she pulled the thin arm.

In the flower garden, full of zinnias, marigolds, bachelor buttons, and black-eyed susans, the two women sat on a concrete-slab bench underneath a willow tree.

"He's gettin worse," Mrs. Bailey said somberly. She was plumpish, three inches shorter than her son. Her lips were hastily painted and almost an O. "Look at that perfectly beautiful marigold," she said, stretching out a sapphire-ringed hand.

"*I* don't know what to tell you." Lottie, so thin the veins bulged dull blue beneath the skin of her arms, usually sighed after she said something. She taught piano in the grammar school and gave private lessons during the summer.

The Alabama sun blazed on the flowers. Mrs. Bailey, despite the fact that she sat under the willow, wore sweat on her brow; she dabbed with a tiny pink handkerchief she carried under her belt.

She turned to Lottie. "What D. B. needs is to get out in the sun. Work in the dirt. It's the war that done it to him."

Lottie's head began to nod as if on a spring. "He don't hardly seem like the same boy. He won't even *speak* to me and it was me taught him piano in the fifth grade."

"He don't even speak to me that brought him into this world half the time." Mrs. Bailey's blue house dress was beginning to stain dark at the arm pits. She had always sweated a good healthy sweat and that was another thing that bothered her about D. B.—he never did sweat. She was careful not to mention this because Lottie didn't sweat much either.

"Oh I could wring that girl's *neck*." Mrs. Bailey clapped her hands together and made a wringing motion.

Lottie knew who she meant. "She'll get her rewards

in the next world, like as not." *She* was Ruthie Sue, D. B.'s former wife that he married just before his two years in the Army. All the time he was in Korea Ruthie Sue wrote him just once, when she thought she was pregnant. ("Been the best thing on earth if she *was,*" Mrs. Bailey had said. "Keep her from runnin around and carryin on so much. But ain't no telling who the daddy woulda been.") Mrs. Bailey and Lottie had talked the whole thing out many times before: how Ruthie Sue moved out of Mrs. Bailey's house ("She was the messiest gal I ever seen," Mrs. Bailey said. "No personal hygiene.") and went back to her mother's over at Yancey, Alabama; how poor D. B. came marching home from the Army and his wife up and said she just didn't want to live with him any more.

"From that day forward," Mrs. Bailey said, digging the dirt with a heel of her shoe, "D. B. just wasn't the same. He wasn't my precious boy any more."

"Suffer in this life," Lottie said, "and live happy in the next."

"Oh if I could only believe that. He just *won't* get a job."

"What does his daddy say?" Lottie thumped a black ant from her leg.

"Oscar just *don't* say. He leaves *all* the worryin to me. You know how quiet Oscar is. Timid, if you ask me, but he don't like for me to say it."

"They ever get a divorce?"

"Unh-unh. D. B. won't talk about it. He just won't *talk.* I'll say D. B. honey, when you gonna get a job? or You ever see Ruthie Sue? or anything like that. He just sets and maybe grunts if he feels like it. *I* don't know what's the matter with him."

"It's probably he's got a frustration," Lottie said, paused, letting Mrs. Bailey take the word in.

"Like as not. And Oscar lets him have the car any night he wants it. Except Wednesday when me and Oscar goes to prayer meetin.'"

Lottie turned her head to Mrs. Bailey, lifted her slight eyebrows and said, "What does he do for *money?* If it's any of my business."

"Oscar gives him a 'lowance, and *I* think he *drinks.*" She put both hands up to her hips and stopped silent. Lottie let her mouth fall open. Finally Mrs. Bailey added, "Homebrew."

"I'll swan," Lottie said, pretending not to believe it.

"He goes off at night with them Rathbone boys, *won't* go to church on Sunday, and gets up about ten o'clock ever morning ill as a hornet. Drinks some black coffee and that's all. It ain't natural, if you ask me."

"It certainly ain't."

"And the awfulest thing, Lottie," and Mrs. Bailey put her hand for an instant on Lottie's knee, "is it's so embarrassing. Him just setting there all day. No job and no plans to get one. *Os*car ain't no help."

"Wish I could talk to you all day but I got a piano student at 'leven o'clock. Baby Wilson. She's as musical as a humming bird." Lottie's face made a smile that showed her even, false teeth.

"That's Queenie Wilson's little girl."

"*So* sweet."

"Let me pick you some marigolds to set on your piano."

In the front yard Lottie, clutching an armful of the yellow and orange flowers, waved goodbye to Mrs. Bailey. Then, "Bye bye, D. B." D. B. yawned and fished for a cigarette.

"D. B. *Bai*ley! She's my best dearest friend."

"Friend schmiend." He flipped the dead match into her camellia bushes.

D. B., holding the newspaper in front of his face, didn't know that his mother had been watching him through the bay window. But he wouldn't have cared one way or the other. He didn't care *what* she did as long as she didn't bother him. That yak-yak-yak got on his nerves. He never had liked her much and every day now he liked her less. Sometimes when she started talking— why don't you do this and why don't you do that—he could feel a fire start in his stomach and then move up through his chest and throat and feel like it was going to come out of his mouth and maybe burn her up. He'd like *that*.

The way D. B. looked at it was this: she'd brought him into the world and she had a responsibility. He'd decided to sit on the front porch as long as he wanted to, and in answer to his mother's question Don't you feel ashamed to get a 'lowance from your daddy at your age? all he could say was Ashamed schmamed. Nosiree he did *not*.

He'd told Cecil Rathbone the night before when they went over to Sipsi Creek to drink homebrew and look for women: "The way I see it is thisaway, when a good job comes up that looks like it's fit for what I'm worth, I'll take it. But I ain't gonna stir till that time. I've fought in the Army and it wasn't my fault I come into the world in the first place." Cecil Rathbone agreed with him and they had a swig of homebrew on it.

The screen door slammed. Out of the corner of his eye he could see his mother go to the other end of the porch and look out at the yard. He knew she was getting ready to say something.

"D. B. sugar."

She was using her nice-as-pie voice. He didn't say a word.

"D. B.?"

He still didn't answer.

"D. B.!"

He stretched both arms, arched his neck. On his right arm just below the shoulder there was a red tattoo: a ragged heart and written under it RUTHIE SUE ONLY YOU.

"What is it you want?" He looked at her. She had her hair pulled back tight and a green cloth tied around it.

"You're just about to drive me *crazy*," she said and drew her mouth down. "Slap dab *crazy*. *Why*? is what I want to know."

"Crud," he said and scratched at the hair emerging over the top of his undershirt.

"What did you say?"

"Crud."

"D. B. *Bailey*! Is that a nasty word?" Her features were contorted to be horrified.

"Crud fud schmud dud cud."

She pretended to fall into the rocker behind her. "Lord God amercy! *What* did I do to deserve this?"

"Ain't no tellin." D. B. was not impressed. "Like as not you murdered some pore innocent baby. And drunk up its blood."

Mrs. Bailey straightened from her slumping position. Her voice was down-to-business: "D. B., I'm gonna get this right straight out with you right now. This whole thing's the silliest thing I ever heard of. And I for one never even *heard* of such a thing. A grown man settin all day on the front porch while his mamma is cookin and workin in the flower garden, not to mention his daddy at the post office. And then gettin a 'lowance not

94

to mention runnin around all night with them Rathbone boys up to no tellin what all over the county. I just ain't gonna put up with it any more." She had talked fast and faster. She stopped a minute to take a long breath, then said, "You understand that plain?"

"I couldn't hear a word you said."

Mrs. Bailey's neck was deep red. "I got a good mind to slap your face."

"Slap it," he said, "you'll get slapped back."

"D. B., I got a good mind to call the law on you."

He lit a cigarette and then spit the loose tobacco out of his mouth.

His mother got up, went to the screen door. She started to open it but came back.

"Sugar," her voice was nice-as-pie again, "why don't you put on a shirt when you set out here? Ain't no tellin what people think." D. B. closed his eyes, bored. "Or why don't you mow the yard or something? Or go work in my flowers in the good honest dirt. My marigolds is just as pretty."

"I ain't foolin with no flowers," he muttered, his eyes still closed.

"Well, put on a *shirt*! I never been so embarrassed in my life as when Lottie come by and you settin here in your underwear and wouldn't even speak to her. Half *neck*id."

"She's saw men all the way neckid, if you ask me."

"D. B. Bailey, I'm gonna slap you. She's my closest dearest friend and ain't no better christian woman in the whole state of Alabama."

D. B. spoke slow, disinterested. "How come old man Edwards used to come trottin out of her house ever mornin? Givin her a Sundy school lesson?"

Mrs. Bailey was already up and slamming the screen door. She called from the living room in a high, unsteady voice, "You're gonna go to hell as sure as the world!"

D. B. opened his eyes. "Hell schmell."

Mr. and Mrs. Bailey had been in bed for almost an hour and a half. It was too hot to sleep. *He* was snoring, of course. Oscar could sleep through anything. She'd always said the Russians could take over the whole town and rape the women-folks and Oscar'd sleep right through it. Long, thin, he lay far over to his side of the bed.

What made her so mad was she had all the worrying to do, he wouldn't do any of it. D. B. off with the car, maybe tearing it up, and Oscar snoring! It made her good and mad.

"Oscar!" she said. She punched him in the ribs with her fist. "Oscar!"

He rolled to his side. "What it it?"

"Oscar, you wake up. I got to talk to you. The very *i*dee, sound asleep and D. B. without a job, settin on the front porch all day and maybe off somewhere tearin up the car with no tellin who. I want you to listen to me!"

"He'll be in after while," Oscar said in a low voice. "We can talk about it in the morning."

"I want to talk about it right now. The very *i*dee."

Oscar got up and, without turning on the lights, found his way to the bath room. Mrs. Bailey was talking all the time:

". . . tell him where to get on and where to get off. It's pagan. In the morning I'm gonna say D. B. we ain't gonna give you no more 'lowance, you've gotta get a job like everbody else, and I ain't gonna have you settin on this front porch where folks can see you. What you think about that, Oscar?" (He was settling back into bed.)

"And I don't want you to give him one penny, don't want you to give him the keys to the car. You oughta heard what he said about Lottie today. You just oughta heard."

She raised her body to pull down her night gown. Oscar closed his eyes.

D. B. sat on the porch, tearing up cigarettes one after another. He sat naked to the waist, his undershirt lying on the floor. He was so mad he couldn't see straight. Before noon the old woman had laid down the law, all about how pagan he was, no more money, no more car, and she said she wouldn't even cook for him. *That* did it —and after he'd been off to the war. At dinnertime she came out to the screen and said in her nice-as-pie voice, "Me and your daddy's gettin ready to eat, D. B. honey. I cooked some turnip greens and field peas and blackberry cobbler—just for me and him." She couldn't have paid him a sack of gold to get his body near that dinner table.

Now she was down in the flower garden digging her good honest dirt. Dirt schmirt and crud fud. He'd fix her up good, some way or other. Yessir. Lost two years of his life for the likes of her—and who brought him to this earth in the first place? he wanted to know. *Her,* and having fun at it.

"D. B. sugar!" That was her calling him from the flower garden. He rubbed a cigarette between his hands, letting the tobacco shreds fall to the porch.

"D. *B.*!"

He turned his body from the waist. "What the hell you want?" he said, not loud enough for her to hear.

She had on an old bonnet and one hand was shielding her eyes from the sun. She moved forward a few steps.

"Come to the edge of the porch," she said, "so I don't have to talk so loud."

He did, almost mechanically.

When he stopped, Mrs. Bailey said, "D. B. sweet, you better be off my porch before your daddy gets home from work. If you ain't, I'm gonna call up the police, honey. I reckon they'll just take you off to the jail and you can set there as long as you want to." She was talking softly and smiling.

Slowly he began to unbuckle his belt, then unzip the fly of his pants. He let the pants fall and stepped out of them, standing in his khaki Army shorts.

"D. B. Bailey what on *earth!*"

Then he ambled slowly down the steps, across the grass to the flower bed where she stood.

"You've gone crazy as a betsy bug," she said, more to herself than to him. She was pulling down at both sides of her bonnet as if to hold her head on.

D. B. stopped still, then moved across the dirt—paying no mind to the flowers—and with one swat to her face knocked her down. She was screaming now but he seemed not to notice. Slowly he knelt beside her, put a knee across her middle, and with one hand pried open her mouth, with the other scooped up dirt and poured it in. Mrs. Bailey made deep, growling sounds.

"Honest schmonest dirt schmirt."

He scooped more dirt and poured it in.

Views

John Telling (called Tell by his former friends at the shoe factory) turned sick at heart when he lost his job (repression, they told him), and sicker still when his wife Naomi left him.

"You are not even interesting," she said to him as she stood before the dresser mirror in their three room apartment.

"I just don't say much," he answered. "I'm interesting inside my head."

She doubted that, she told him and adjusted her hat. "Here's five dollars," she said as she left with her suitcase. She carried with her their savings of a hundred twenty dollars.

He decided that before he looked for a job he'd devote one week of his life to something important. He had sent long essay-stories to *Harper's, Atlantic, New Yorker, Esquire,* and eventually to *True Confessions.*

He told what he thought was wrong with the world (mainly that nobody loved; sex was impure), what he thought about God (God was something he'd actually seen—a vague gray form—at five o'clock in the morning), what he thought about his wife, her mother, his own dead mother. And much more.

He received rejection slips always, never even a handwritten note.

There was one place on earth, though, where people read whatever there was to read—in public restrooms. That might be the place to write out his VIEWS.

Of course there were drawbacks; he wrote them all down to consider them.

1. Short time. Janitors usually scrub walls every day.
2. Danger of getting picked up by a cop.
3. Obscenity that might appear beside VIEWS.
4. Unpleasant odor.

But his views might help somebody, especially a bum or alcoholic or dope addict, people who hung around such places. He'd have to take care to choose the right place.

He spent a day visiting various hotel restrooms, the City Court House, the Greyhound Station. Finally he chose the restroom of the Arching Bus Lines because he noticed that the marble walls of the compartments hadn't been washed in several days. They were covered with filthy verses and drawings. He checked the doors and all of them would lock; he could have privacy.

On the first day, Monday, he chose the stall nearest the outside door to begin with. He took several paper napkins, soaked them with water and soap powder, and went to work. After the last picture had been scrubbed away, he stood up and began to write:

My mother was dear to me. She was a very religious woman—IN HER WAY. When I was nine years old she told me this is a short life, full of great sorrow, and the one business you've got in it is to find God. One way or another.

It is a hard thing to find God. I went to sea to find him. I did not find him in China or South America. I found him a few years ago at five o'clock in the morning as I went to work at the shoe factory. He was grey, something like mist, and he spoke to me in a clear, loud voice. You must love everybody, he said. PURELY. But I'll write more about God later on. It is not so much FINDING God as TRYING to find him.

At this point John Telling stood back and read his work. He sat for a while and rested; someone tried the door.

Till noon he wrote about his adventures at sea, the Chinese girl he met and loved for a while. It was the first time he had really loved anybody except his mother, and it was the first time he had even come close to finding God.

THE PURITY OF SEX CAN BE RELIGIOUS, he wrote.

At noon he took off for an hour and had hamburgers and milk in the cafe of the bus station. An old man wearing a torn coat sat down next to him at the counter.

"What do you think about God?" John Telling asked before he had even considered the impropriety of the question. He had never asked such a thing of a stranger.

The old man went on noisily eating his soup.

"I said, what do you think about God?"

"I don't think he's worth a damn," the old man answered.

John Telling was saddened but in a way pleased. It was just such an old man as this that the VIEWS might help.

That afternoon Telling wrote on the second wall, for the most part about his wife Naomi. He decided to give the full experience of his meeting with God, only not now. On the last day, in the last stall.

He had met Naomi in a bar, because back then, seven years ago, he drank a lot. He was working at the shoe factory and every night he went to this bar and drank beer. There was this pretty, black-haired girl who came every night also and drank with anybody who'd buy her a drink. Usually at closing time she'd leave with one of the men. Most of them were laborers.

This hurt John Telling because he thought the girl was throwing her life away. She'd never find love. There was no purity of sex in her life. Drunken sex was not ever pure. Furthermore you had to sacrifice for love. There had to be challenges.

He began to sit with the girl and buy her drinks. Her name was Naomi. She began to leave with him at closing time. After a month he asked her to marry him and she did.

From the start she said she didn't like him very much. This was important because it was a challenge to him and the TRYING. She thought his ideas were nutty, and that was the word she used. He knew that she was afraid of his ideas because people are always afraid of the highest FORM.

One night she was getting ready to go out and drink, he wrote on the wall, and I begged her not to go out. Why? she said. Because I want to discover you and you ought to want to discover me. This way through love we can discover God. You can go to hell, she told me. This did not bother me because it made the challenge greater than ever. When she came home that night she was drunk and wouldn't let me sleep in the bed with her. I've had my fun, she said. For a week I slept in a chair, and then off and on she would let me sleep with her. But I never got mad at her—I never did. I knew that to get mad might make her leave me. Then I'd have to start on another challenge.

John Telling wrote how she hit him with a skillet and he had to lay off work for three days. How she made fun of his religion. And about her mother, who lived a bad life for a woman of sixty and tried to get Naomi to put him in an asylum. But even Naomi's mother became a challenge to him. He typed six pages of instructions and sent them to her by mail.

Visibly his life was a failure, he wrote on the wall. His wife had left him, for one thing. But INVISIBLY no it was not. His main reason for saying this was that he had met God. Which he would explain fully in the last stall. And whoever wanted to could read about it there.

By six o'clock he had covered the two side walls. He was tired and his back ached from stooping, but he decided that instead of going to the apartment to rest, he'd look for a challenge. That was the one thing that gave meaning to life, that was the thing that led to God. He searched through several bars, all of them full of B-girls and dark, before he found the right bar with the right girl. She was young and pretty—he knew she worked for the house—and she rubbed his leg as they talked.

"Your first time in here, I'll bet," she said.

"Yes," he said, "in a way. I've been here before but not this exact place."

"You're funny," she said. "I'll bet you're a deep one."

"No, but I'm searching for a challenge. I have a purpose."

She told him about her friend Nelda who got fired the day before. Nelda had had three children and she gave them all away.

"They should have been her challenge," he said. "She was not religious."

"She reads the Bible all the time. She's read it all the way through four times."

"That's not what I mean," he said. Then he began to tell her some of his VIEWS. This wasn't the thing he usually did—at least till he knew the person well, but he was excited, he felt on the brink of something.

At last she said, "Gonna buy me a drink, honey? I've got to make a living."

"Don't you want to hear how I met God?"

"I've got to make a living," she said. "Buy me a drink or not?" She smiled and rubbed his leg.

"I can't afford another one."

"Sorry, honey." She got up and walked to the back of the bar.

The next morning he arrived at the Arching Bus Lines just at eight o'clock. As he went into the restroom he saw that the door of the first stall was open and then that a young man in blue jeans was scrubbing the walls.

"You can't do that." John Telling caught his arm. "These are my VIEWS."

"Are you the crazy son of a bitch?" the janitor said.

John Telling grabbed him by his shirt and pulled him out of the stall.

He lowered his voice and said, "I haven't even got to God yet. You don't know how important this is."

"I'll knock your crazy head off," the janitor said.

John Telling let go of the shirt, rushed for the last stall and locked himself in.

"Get out of there!" the janitor said. He pounded on the door. "You gonna get out of there?"

There was silence for a while and John Telling was well into his first paragraph, preparing for God, when a heavy blow struck against the door. A loud voice said, "This is the law! Open the goddamn door!"

John was still writing, and still preparing for God, when he saw the blue-suited man climbing over the top.

This is My Living Room

It ain't big but big enough for me and my family—
my wife Rosie setting over there reading recipes in the
Birmingham *News* and my two girls Ellen Jean and
Martha Kay watching the TV. I am setting here holding
Life magazine in my lap. I get *Life,* the *News,* and *Christian Living.* I read a lots, the newspaper everyday from
cover to cover. I don't just look at the pictures in *Life.*
I read what's under them and the stories. I consider
myself a smart man and I ain't bragging. A man can learn
a lots from just watching the TV, if he knows what to
watch for and if he listens close. I do. There ain't many
that can say that and be truthful. Maybe nobody else in
this whole town which is Pine Springs.

Yonder in the corner, to the other side of the Coca-
Cola calendar, is my 12 guage. When I go in to bed, I
take it with me, set it against the wall, loaded, ready to
use, so I can use it if I need to. I've used it before and
maybe will again. The only one to protect you is yourself
and if you don't you're a fool. I got me a pistol and a .22
locked up in the back room. I could use them too. Rosie
can shoot, I taught her how, but she's afraid. The noise
scares her. She said, Don't make me shoot that thing one
more time. We was in the forest. The girls was waiting
for us in the car. Don't make me shoot that thing again,
she said, and started to cry. I slapped her face and told
her to shoot the rifle. She did. Then I took it and told
her to go back to the car with the girls. She started to cry
again, but I stayed a long time—till it was dark—and shot
the rifle and pistol and shot gun.

You can't tell what people are going to do in a
town like this. They want your money and they're jealous
of you. They talk about you in front of the court house

and plan up schemes. You can't trust the police or sheriff. You got to watch out for yourself.

MY TWO GIRLS

are 14 and 16 year old. Both of them want to go on dates but I won't let them. I know what the boys will do, what they want to get out of a girl.

Ellen Jean, the oldest, is a right good-looking girl but sassy and you can't hardly do anything with her. She started to paint her face at school, so I took her out. I've got her working at my store.

I see her passing notes to Elbert. I seen her get out of his car one night. She said she was going to the picture show by herself. She's a born liar and sassy. Like as not he's had her. Like as not she's got a baby starting in her belly right now. She's a sassy bitch-girl and don't take after her ma or me. Sometimes I wonder if she's mine.

Martha Kay is like her ma. She cries all the time, minds good. I let her stay in high school and will keep on letting her as long as she can act right. The first time I see lipstick, out she comes. She can work at the store too. I could use her to dust and sweep up. You can always use somebody to keep things clean.

I ask Martha Kay, Why're you late gettin in from school? Where you been? Off in the woods with some boy? She starts to cry. She's like her ma.

Martha Kay helps at the store on Saturdays but can't add up figures good.

Ellen Jean is watching that man on TV make a fool of hisself and she's laughing. She'll end up a Birmingham whore. Her sister is laughing too and they look like a bunch of fools.

PEOPLE

in this town are like they are in any other town on earth. I was in the World War I and seen a good many places. Since then I've stayed here most of the time. What's the good of moving? People are as mean one place as they are another and they're always out to get you. They won't get me because I won't let them.

Take Sam Coates who owed me $20 for that fencing. Sam wouldn't pay. I said to him pay up by first of the month or I'll make you pay. He says how will I make him. Sue him for $20? Won't no lawyer in town take it anyway, he says, because they're all looking out for election. You pay, I told him.

When first of the month come I got in my car and rode out in the country to his front door. Where is your husband? I said to his wife. Milking, she said, and I went around to the barn with my .22, stuck it in his face, and told him to pay me or I'd blow the hell out of him. Sam turned as white as that bucket of milk. Him and his wife counted me out the money.

There ain't a one on earth that wouldn't try to cheat you if they could.

I use to think that women was worse than men but now I think just the opposite. Women are easier to handle. About the worst they can do is talk and what does that matter?

Niggers are better than anybody because you can handle them. They don't hardly ever give you any trouble. Except that one time with Ezmo. I didn't have no trouble handling him.

MY STORE

is about the best thing I know of. It seems like a human being sometimes except a lots better because you can trust it.

I've got as much business as I need and make more profit than some people I know of. Maybe they've got better houses and ride in finer cars, but maybe they didn't make all their money like I did. Honest. I ain't earned a cent crooked. I didn't inherit my money. I worked for it.

Country folks and niggers is my customers. Saturday is my big day. Ellen Jean helps me all through the week and Martha Kay helps out on Saturday. They're not much help. Don't take the right kind of interest.

I like the smell of my store from the time I open it up at 7 in the morning till the time Ellen Jean throws oil sand on the floor when it's time to sweep up. I like everything about that store.

I sell canned goods, fresh meat, bread and crackers, flour, fencing, nails, hammers, guns. I sell all the things a body could need.

Not like at Admore's where it's just women's hats and dresses, or Taylor's where it's just for younguns.

I want to know what the world is coming to.

If Rosie ever dies and the girls go off I'll sell this house and sleep in my store. I'll put up a cot, take my guns and my clothes and that's all. Maybe the TV.

What do I care about this house.

THIS LIVING ROOM

ain't no part of my body or my mind. The lace on the mantel-piece, what's it for? That nigger youngun wetting on a commode with Mobile wrote on it, what's it for? Them pictures of movie stars in silver frames. This light-colored linoleum you can't step on without it leaving a mark from your heel. Them silky-laced curtains.

One time I took my hand across the mantel and knocked off Rosie's big clock and a vase full of flowers. Rosie set in here and cried half the night—till I got up and told her to get in bed with her husband where she belonged.

PEOPLE,

your own flesh and blood, will try to run over you, stomp you, steal from you, kill you if they can.

Take the law. A body would think—if he wasn't very smart—that a man of law was a good man. It ain't so. 90 per cent of the time it ain't so. A body says then, if the law ain't good, who is? Nobody.

Sheriff Claine is a good example. He use to be always poking around my store, making hints. Standing outside the front window part of the time. One evening late I got in my car and followed the Sheriff Claine— down the highway towards Brushwood, then off down the country road towards Glory Church, and then he stopped. I stopped a good piece behind him and followed him through a pine thicket to a liquor still. A whole big wild-cat set-up. Sheriff Claine was the ringleader of the bunch.

Next time he come to my store, I said, Sheriff, finding much wild-cat whiskey? He grunted and pulled up his belt and let on like business was slow. Somebody said, and I eased it to him, they's a big still down towards Glory Church, off in a pine thicket.

Sheriff Claine couldn't talk for a minute and squinted his eyes. I'll have a look, he said.

Oh, probably ain't nothing to it, I told him. I ain't gonna mention it to nobody, nosir, not to a soul.

The police is just like him. They hide out at night and sleep when they're suppose to be patroling. I've caught them at it.

Sheriff Claine didn't give me no trouble about Ezmo. He listened to what I said here at the house and that was that.

OLD EZMO

was what you'd call a low class of nigger. He'd come into the store and say, Give me a pound of sugar and I'll pay you Saturday evening. I wouldn't do it. I'd say, You give me the money. I give you the best prices in town. You give me the money.

One time Ellen Jean let him have a loaf of bread on credit. I smacked her for it and told her she was a fool, which she is. On Saturday Ezmo come in and wanted some side meat for cooking greens. Pay me off, I told him, for that loaf of bread. What loaf? he wanted to know.

Ellen Jean, didn't you charge this nigger a loaf of bread? She said yes and he said she didn't. You ain't calling my girl a liar, are you? Naw, he said, but he didn't get no loaf of bread. Somebody's a liar, I told him, and it ain't my girl.

He said he wouldn't pay me. You're a crooked, low-down nigger, I told him, and they ain't nothing much worse than that. You ain't fit for making side meat out of. I told him if he had any younguns he better watch out. I didn't want lots of black bastards like him growing up in my town. You get out of here right now.

That night I was setting in this chair where I am right now—this same chair. The girls was watching TV. Rosie was shelling peas.

I heard somebody outdoors and I knew right off who it was. I got better ears than most people. Any time somebody sets foot in this yard, I know it. Even if I'm asleep.

That's Ezmo, I said to myself. I got up, picked up my 12 gauge over in the corner and said I was gonna clean it, went through the house without turning any lights on, then eased out the back door.

There wasn't much moon but I spotted Ezmo right off, standing behind some hedge bushes over by my bedroom window. I got just this side of him without him hearing. EZMO! I hollered, and up he come with a knife about 8 inches long. I was ready for him. I triggered my 12 gauge and got him square in the face.

Rosie and the girls come running to the back door. Get me a flashlight, I told them. I never seen such a blowed-up face. The girls started getting sick and Rosie started crying. I want you to take a good look, I told Rosie, and see what this world is coming to. You see that knife he had. I held Rosie's arm and made her stand there till Ellen Jean could get Sheriff Claine.

ROSIE

ain't exactly good-looking. She's got to be dried-up but once was on the fat side. She makes a good wife. I've been married to her for going on 30 year. Sometimes I get fed up with her and go to my woman in South Town. I take her a couple of cans of beans and some hose or a pair of bloomers. There ain't nothing much a woman won't do for food or clothes.

Rosie knows about her, all about her. I talk about it sometimes when we're in bed. I wouldn't trade Rosie for her but Rosie don't know that.

Tomorrow's Saturday and I got to get some sleep.

"Turn off the TV, girls. Get in yonder to bed. Tomorrow's Saturday."

I stand in front of Rosie. "Go in yonder and get in bed." She starts to cry and that's all right. It wouldn't be a bit like her if she didn't.